QUEEN'S COUNSEL

C000025507

QUEEN'S COUNSEL 2

Judgment Day

BY STEUART & FRANCIS

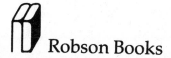

Robson Books

First published in Great Britain in 1997 by Robson Books Ltd, Bolsover House, 5-6 Clipstone Street, London W1P 8LE

Copyright © 1997 Alex Steuart Williams and Graham Francis Defries The right of Alex Steuart Williams and Graham Francis Defries to be identified as author of this work has been asserted by them in accordance with the Copyright, Designs and Patents Act 1988

British Library Cataloguing in Publication Data
A catalogue record for this title is available from the British Library

ISBN 1 86105 128 X

All rights reserved. No part of this publication may be reproduced, stored in a retrieval system, or transmitted in any form or by any means, electronic, mechanical, photocopying, recording or otherwise, without the prior permission in writing of the publishers.

Printed by The Guernsey Press Company Limited, Guernsey, Channel Islands

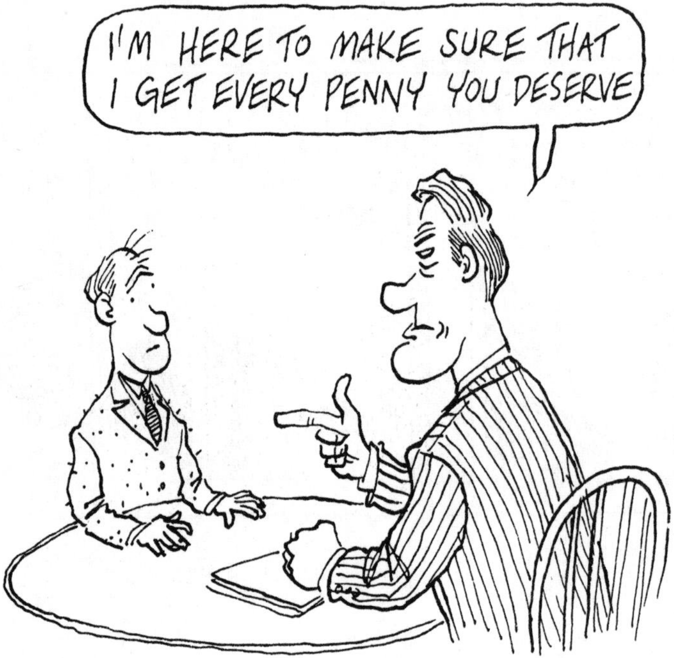
I'M HERE TO MAKE SURE THAT I GET EVERY PENNY YOU DESERVE

BRITAIN'S FAVOURITE
HANGING JUDGE

AUGUST 1995 THE FEATURE FILM "JUDGE DREDD"

IS RELEASED IN THE UK

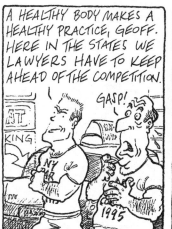

SEPTEMBER 1995. NICK LEESON, THE "ROGUE TRADER" WHO BROKE BARINGS BANK, IS IMPRISONED IN SINGAPORE PENDING TRIAL.

SEPTEMBER 1995. THE NEWS OF THE WORLD PUBLISHES VIDEOTAPE OF MR JUSTICE THORNTON IN EMBARRASSING CIRCUMSTANCES.

WELL MR. SPROCKETT, THIS IS PRIMA FACIE A CLEAR CASE, INTER ALIA, OF RES IPSA LOQUITUR.

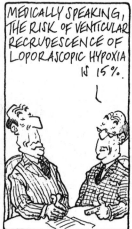

MEDICALLY SPEAKING, THE RISK OF VENTICULAR RECRUDESCENCE OF LOPORASCOPIC HYPOXIA IS 15%.

ENGINEERING ANALYSIS SHOWS THAT PERIPHERAL TRANSMISSION OF THE CIRCUMFERENTIAL AXIS BIAS-BELTED THE STUB AXLE MOUNT.

WELL, THAT JUST ABOUT CONCLUDES THE CONFERENCE, GENTLEMEN.

... EVERYTHING QUITE CLEAR, MR SPROCKETT?

OH YES, QUITE CLEAR, THANKYOU.

OCTOBER 1995. O.J. SIMPSON FOUND NOT GUILTY.

NOVEMBER 1995. THE BAR IS ACCUSED OF SEX DISCRIMINATION.

TABLOID NEWSPAPERS COURT CONTROVERSY BY PAYING WITNESSES IN THE ROSEMARY WEST TRIAL FOR THEIR "EXCLUSIVE" STORIES. NOVEMBER 1995.

TERRY VENABLES, CAPTAIN OF THE ENGLAND FOOTBALL TEAM, RESIGNS TO SPEND MORE TIME WITH HIS LAWYERS. JANUARY 1996.

JANUARY 1996. A SUBSTANTIAL CLAIM FOR DAMAGES ADDS TO THE DUCHESS OF YORK'S FINANCIAL DIFFICULTIES.

LORD JUSTICE SCOTT'S LONG-AWAITED REPORT CRITICISES THE GOVERNMENT'S HANDLING OF THE ARMS-TO-IRAQ AFFAIR. FEBRUARY 1996.

JUDGE SIGNS GAGGING ORDER

Panel 1: I DON'T KNOW WHY THE OPPOSITION HAVE MADE SUCH A FUSS ABOUT THE LATE DISCLOSURE OF THE REPORT.

SCOTT REPORT —LATEST

Panel 2: IT'S UP TO THE CROWN TO DECIDE WHEN TO DISCLOSE ITS CONTENTS.

Panel 3: IT'S ALL A STORM IN A TEACUP —THERE'S NOTHING MUCH IN HIS REPORT ANYWAY.

Panel 4: THE DEFENCE OBJECT TO THE CROWN'S LATE DISCLOSURE OF THIS EXPERT REPORT, YOUR HONOUR.

SIR GEOFFREY, YOU CAN'T JUST DUMP THIS ON THE COURT AT THE LAST MINUTE!

HMPH!

THE LORD CHANCELLOR'S DIVORCE REFORM BILL IS WIDELY BUT WRONGLY REPORTED AS PERMITTING CHILDREN TO PREVENT THEIR PARENTS' DIVORCE. FEBRUARY 1996.

ALTERNATIVE DISPUTE RESOLUTION

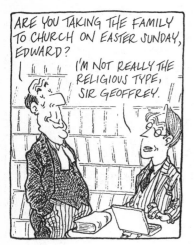

YOU HAVE AN EXCELLENT CASE, MR SPROCKETT. I ADVISE YOU TO COMMENCE PROCEEDINGS AT ONCE.

DON'T WORRY, MR SPROCKETT, —YOU MUSTN'T GIVE UP NOW. YOU HAVE A VERY GOOD CHANCE OF SUCCESS.

DAILY COURT LIST
SPROCKETT —v— PARKINSON

I'M CAUTIOUSLY OPTIMISTIC ABOUT TODAY'S TRIAL, MR SPROCKETT.

I CAN'T BELIEVE WE LOST! I'M RUINED!

I ALWAYS SAID THIS WAS A MOST DIFFICULT CASE. LITIGATION IS SO RISKY.

LOOK AT THIS, GEOFFREY, THIS MAGAZINE I FOUND IN OUR SON'S ROOM.

YOU'RE RESPONSIBLE FOR THIS! ITS... DISGUSTING!

WHERE? WHAT IS?

IN HIS SOCK DRAWER... WRAPPED IN PLAIN BROWN PAPER... I CAN'T BEAR TO LOOK AT IT!

"THE LAW SOCIETY GAZETTE"

WHY CAN'T HE READ THE BEANO LIKE NORMAL 12-YEAR OLDS?

WE'VE GOT A CAST-IRON ALIBI THIS TIME, MR LONGWIND. THE DEFENDANT WAS AT THE BETTING SHOP WHEN THE ROBBERY TOOK PLACE — AND HIS BOOKIE WILL BE A WITNESS.

I DON'T THINK THE JURY WILL LIKE THE BETTING SHOP MUCH, RICHARD.

I SUPPOSE YOU'RE RIGHT.

TAP TAP

WHISPER....

ER... ACTUALLY HE WAS LOOKING AFTER HIS MOTHER-IN-LAW ALL EVENING, AND SHE'LL BE A WITNESS INSTEAD.

EXCELLENT

HOW TO TRANSLATE A
LEGAL OPINION:

THE LAW IN THIS AREA IS
DOGGED BY CONFUSION.

I WISH I
UNDERSTOOD THIS
BRIEF A LITTLE
BETTER

THIS CLAIM IS SUPPORTED BY
THE AUSTRALIAN CASE OF
O'ROURKE -v- N.S.WALES
PIG BREEDERS.

THERE'S
NO U.K. AUTH-
ORITY WE CAN
RELY ON

RECOVERY OF DAMAGES
IS LIKELY TO BE SUBSTANTIAL

THE LEGAL
COSTS, MORE
LIKELY

...IN CONCLUSION, THIS CASE
CERTAINLY MERITS SUPPORT
FROM PUBLIC FUNDS.

ONLY AN
IDIOT WOULD
RISK THEIR
OWN MONEY
ON THIS.

ALL=NEW LEGAL AID
APPLICATION FORMS:

APPLICATION FOR
LEGAL AID.
DO YOU:
Q.1. DO YOU:
(a) HAVE NO MONEY?
(b) HAVE LOTS OF MONEY?
(b) LIVE IN A LARGE
HOUSE WITH SERVANTS
AND FOUR CARS AND
YET HAVE NO MONEY?

Q2. ARE YOU:
(a) DESERVING OF PUBLIC
FUNDS?
(b) UNDESERVING?
(c) HIDING YOUR ASSETS
IN AN OFFSHORE
ACCOUNT?

Q.3. ARE YOU:
(a) GUILTY?
(b) NOT GUILTY?
(c) BLAMING IT ON
SOMEONE ELSE,
PREFERABLY A
DECEASED RELATIVE?

Q.4. HOW WOULD YOU
LIKE YOUR LEGAL
AID TO BE PAID?
(a) BY CHEQUE.
(b) BY DIRECT DEBIT.
(c) IN USED BANKNOTES.

© HMSO. 1996